Garden Beetles

An introduction to those little-known and unsung ecological
activists which abound in all our gardens and allotments

DARREN J. MANN & CHRISTOPHER O'TOOLE

Research Officers, Hope Entomological Collections,
Oxford University Museum of Natural History

Osmia Publications Limited

First published in 2004 by Osmia Publications, Ltd.,
Osmia House, 42 Mountsorrel Lane, Leicestershire LE12 7NF, UK.

© Osmia Publications 2004

ISBN 1-904770-08-8

A CIP record for this title is available from the British Library.

Cover photograph: A Maculate Longhorn, *Strangalia maculata* (Family: Cerambycidae), feeding at hogweed flowers. © Clive R. Turner.

Production by Osmia Publications Ltd.

Artwork by MJU Graphics, Quorn, Leicestershire.

Printed and bound in Thailand by Gift Export Co. Ltd.

About the authors

Darren J. Mann works in the Hope Entomological Collections of the Oxford University Museum of Natural History. Here, he is Collections Manager of the extensive insect collections.

Beetles have been a passion in Darren's life for more than twenty years and his specialist research interests are centred on the taxonomy (classification) and ecology of dung beetles and flower-visiting chafers. He also has an interest in cockroaches and is generally interested in, and is a recognised expert on, the principles of insect collection management.

Darren's research interests have taken him to the foothills of the Himalayas, the deserts of Namibia, the forests of Bolivia and the rice paddies of The Gambia.

Chris O'Toole also works in the Hope Entomological Collections of the Oxford University Museum of Natural History. His research interests include the systematics and floral relations of bees in the Middle East and the biodiversity of native bees in South American and African savannas. His interest in the biodiversity of bees has taken him to Central and South America, the deserts of North America and the Middle East. He is particularly interested in the systematics and biology of bees that have potential as managed pollinators of crops, as alternatives to the honeybee.

Chris has collaborated in the making of many natural history films about insects and has published 15 books for the popular market on insect behaviour and natural history.

Acknowledgements

Darren Mann: I would like to thank Tony Chippendale, whose gift of a butterfly net at an early age got me first started. I would also like to thank George McGavin, Max Barclay, John Deeming, Chris O'Toole, Ben Woodcock, James Hogan, Steve Lane and John Ismay, whose knowledge and discussions about entomology keep me enthused. Thanks also to Andrew Salisbury whose extensive knowledge of garden entomology was invaluable. Finally, a special thanks to my big sister Mel for everything.

Chris O'Toole: I thank my wife Rose for tolerating with good humour my obsession with insects and for her never-ending support.

Contents

Living in the Age of Beetles 1

We live in the Age of Beetles.

E.A. Evans & C.L. Bellamy, 2000, *An Inordinate Fondness for Beetles*

Introduction

The 'true' beetles first appear in the fossil record during the Triassic period, about 240 million years ago, making them contemporaries of the dinosaurs. They were a dominant part of the insect fauna of the Mesozoic (245-65 mya). Since then, the group has diversified into many species and varied forms and it is now the most species rich group of animals on the planet. There are more than 350,000 named species of beetles and this accounts for about 30% of all animal species. More surprisingly, perhaps, beetles represent 1 in 5 of all living things! Indeed, aliens visiting our planet might reasonably conclude that, on sheer numbers of both species and individuals, beetles, rather than people, are the dominant life form on Earth. As we shall see, this dominance is reflected in the wide range of ecological services beetles provide: they occupy keystone positions in the network of ecological relationships that underpin almost all habitats.

One of the most famous quotes about beetles, though some people say he never said it, originates from the English biologist J.B.S. Haldane (1892-1964). When asked what might be learned about the Creator by examining the natural world, his response was "An inordinate fondness for beetles." Indeed, it is often said that an interest in beetles inspired Charles Darwin to study evolution.

What are beetles?

Beetles belong to the Class of animals called the Insecta, this, along with the Arachnida (spiders and scorpions), Myriapoda (millipedes and centipedes) and Crustacea (crabs, shrimps and woodlice) make up the Arthropoda or 'jointed legged animals'. The insects are recognised by having three parts to body (head, thorax, abdomen), three pairs of legs (on the thorax), a pair of antennae, and when present, two pairs of wings.

Within the Insecta, beetles comprise the great order Coleoptera. Other familiar orders are the Lepidoptera (butterflies and moths) and the Hymenoptera (ants, wasps and bees). Beetles are found almost everywhere throughout the world, except in Antarctica and in every habitat, apart from the open seas and are most species rich and diverse in the tropics. They range in size from the minute feather-wing beetles (Family Ptiliidae), the adults of which can be as small as 0.25mm long, to the giant, tropical longhorn beetles (Family Cerambycidae), which can up to 200mm in length.

The name Coleoptera is derived from the Greek *koleos*, for sheath and *pteron*, for wing; this refers to their hardened forewings (called wing cases or elytra), which is one of the key characteristics of the group. It is these hardened wing cases that are believed to be the secret of beetles' success, because they protect the membranous hind-wings from damage. This has allowed the beetles to exploit every nook and cranny in the environment. In some families, such as the rove beetles (Staphylinidae), the elytra are much shorter than the abdomen, though they still meet in the midline and cover the elaborately folded wings.

However, there are a few beetles in which the elytra are completely absent, such as in the Lampyridae or glow worms, in which the females are larviform and resemble the immature, larval stages.

The following combination of characters distinguishes beetles from most other insects, though the reader is directed to the more comprehensive identification guides in the references. See also Fig. 1

- Forewings modified to form hardened elytra
- Elytra meet in the middle of the body
- Hind-wings membranous, folded under elytra
- Mandibulate (biting/chewing) mouthparts
- Palps present (though may be very small)
- Antennae with 11 segments (or fewer)
- Prothorax usually large and distinct
- Tarsi with 4-5 segments (sometimes 3)

The most likely group of insects to be confused with the Coleoptera are the true bugs (Order Hemiptera, suborder Heteroptera), which include the well-known shield bugs. However, true bugs can be separated from beetles by the way the wings overlap and have a membranous tip. In this way the wings do not meet at the midline, as with beetles. A second separating feature is that all true bugs have needle-like 'sucking' mouthparts with no palps at the base, unlike the palps and biting jaws of the beetles. The wings of most bugs also exhibit a distinctive pattern of veins, which is absent from beetles' elytra. Earwigs (Order Dermaptera) can sometimes be mistaken for rove beetles (Staphylinidae), since they have shortened elytra. However, earwigs have only three tarsal segments, antennae usually with more than eleven segments and the tip of the abdomen ends in a pair of pincers or forceps.

There are numerous opinions on the classification within the order Coleoptera, with estimates of the total number of species ranging from 1 to 5 million; there isn't even a consensus on the total number of families, with, according to authority, anything from 148 to 173 families.

There are four suborders of beetles:

- The **Archostemata** are believed to be the most primitive beetles. There are just four families, with about 28 species, all of which are associated with decaying wood where they feed on fungi.

- The **Myxophaga** contains just four families containing around 94 species of small beetles (<3mm) that occur in aquatic and riparian habitats, where they feed on algae.

- The **Adephaga** contains 10 families, including the well-known ground beetles (Carabidae) and the diving beetles (Dytiscidae). Most of the 60,000 species are generalist predators, with a small number of seed, fungus or algal feeders. The group has two terrestrial and eight aquatic families.

- The **Polyphaga** contains the remaining 130 or so families and 85% of all beetle species. They occur in all habitats and occupy almost every niche. There are predacious, phytophagous, mycophagous, saprophagous, and even parasitic species.

Life cycle

All beetles have a complete metamorphosis and are thus said to be holometabolous. That is, they pass through four stages: egg (ovum), larva (3-6 instars), pupa and finally the adult. The larva and pupa correspond, respectively, to the caterpillar and chrysalis stages of butterflies and moths.

In most temperate regions beetles pass though one life cycle per year (univoltine), though in favourable years they sometimes manage a second. According to species, beetles can pass through cold winters in any one of the four stages.

Egg

Beetles lay eggs singly or in batches, most often in and around the larval food. In most leaf-eating beetles, eggs batches are laid batches on the underside of host-plant leaves. In some woodborers, the female lays her eggs inside the wood by drilling into it with a hardened egg laying tube or ovipositor. In the oil beetles (Family Meloidae), the female lays several hundred eggs in a small depression in the ground under plants.

In most species, once the eggs are laid, the female leaves but in some groups this in not the case. Female tortoise beetles (Chrysomelidae) guard their eggs against attack from predators and parasitoids, often chasing away the would-be foe.

Larva

The larva is the main feeding stage. Beetle larvae have mostly 3 - 4 larval instars. However, in the skin beetles (Family Dermestidae), larval development can be extended up to 6 instars when food is scarce. The larval stage of some soil or wood dwelling species, such as stag beetles (Family Lucanidae) and longhorn beetles (Family Cerambycidae) can extend over 5 years, even though the adults live only for a few months. In some very large longhorns and jewel beetles (Family Buprestidae), the larval stage may last as long as 9 - 12 years. At the other end of the scale, the small rove beetle *Phanerota fasciata* can complete its three larval instars in just over three days!

Pupa

The pupal stage is often referred to as the resting stage, but this quite inaccurate. Within the pupae, the entire body contents are reorganised from larval to adult structures, an amazing feat of engineering! The pupa often looks like a mummified adult beetle and is often attached to the underside of suitable host plant leaves, or enclosed in a pupal chamber, made from the surrounding substrate. In some groups, the final instar larva spins a tough, silk cocoon.

Adult

As in all insects, the adult is the dispersal and reproductive stage. Some adult beetles don't feed and only live a short time; others can live for several seasons. Indeed, the adults of some species are remarkably long-lived. For example, adults of the ground beetle *Carabus auronitens* (Carabidae) can live for over 7 years. Each species will also have its own flight period. Some species may emerge from hibernation in early spring and live a few months, while others may only appear for a few weeks in early summer.

What do beetles eat?

While the majority of beetle species are plant-feeders, many are carnivorous and prey on other animals, mostly insects and other invertebrates such as slugs, snails and earthworms. However, some, such as the larger aquatic diving beetles, feed, as larvae, on fish, tadpoles and newts. Many species eat detritus and decaying organic matter of both animal and plant origin and are said to be saprophagous. Some beetles are necrophagous and specialise on dead animal tissue as food, a fact reflected in the generic name of the species commonly called burying or sexton beetles, *Nicrophorus*.

Other beetles are mycophagous and specialise in eating fungi and there are even some parasitic species.

Some vital statistics

The largest beetles are the tropical:
Titanus giganteus (Cerambycidae): length 150-200mm.
Dynastes hercules (Scarabaeidae): length 150-180mm, weighing up to 88 gm.
Goliathus goliathus (Scarabaeidae): length 80mm, weighing up to 100 gm.
Beetles over 100mm in length are only found in two families, the Cerambycidae and the Scarabaeidae. 20 families contain beetles over 50mm.
The smallest beetles include *Nanosella fungi* (Ptiliidae): 0.25 mm, weighing just 0.4 mg!

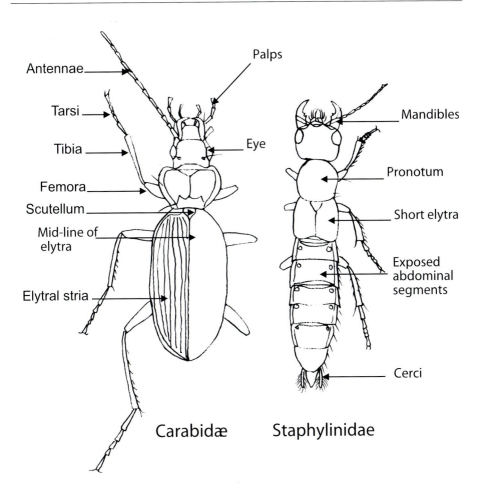

Carabidæ   Staphylinidae

Fig. 1. A ground beetle (Carabidae, left) and a rove beetle (Staphylinidae, right), showing the main features and body parts if beetles. © Darren J. Mann

There are 46 beetle families containing species with a total length of less than 1mm.
On a world basis, the most species rich families are the:
Curculionidae (weevils): 60,000 species.
Staphylinidae (rove beetles): 46,000 species.
The families with fewest species are the:
Phloiophilidae (slime mould beetle): 1 species.
Sphaeritidae (false clown beetles): 4 species.

Beetles and people 2

Beetles in folklore

Beetles have held the imagination of humans for thousands of years, inspiring numerous myths and some are even religious icons. Today they are collected by enthusiasts, used by scientists to investigate the mechanisms of evolution and as bio-indicators in studies of biodiversity, global warming and many other branches of conservation ecology.

The Devil's coach horse, *Staphylinus olens* (Plate 3) is a well-known garden beetle and has a place in Irish mythology as a symbol of corruption; apparently, it can kill, merely on sight. Scarab beetles are used as shamanic symbols by native peoples of South America and have symbolic importance in Taoism, the mystical philosophy of China.

However, scarabs are best known for their significance in the culture of Ancient Egypt. Here, the "sacred" scarab symbolises the Sun God, Khepri. The particular scarabs involved are frequently seen rolling balls of dung and it is thought that this symbolism arose through association of the dung ball with the sun. Some Egyptian scholars have even suggested that the practice of mummification was inspired by observations of the life history of scarabs, and that the mummy mimics the pupal stage of the beetle, through which the resurrection of the person (metamorphosis of the scarab) is secured (e.g. see discussion in Camberfort, 1994).

In the past, huge quantities of beetles were harvested for use as a source of dyestuffs for the textile industry. Large numbers of conspicuous, metallic-coloured species are still used as ornaments in many parts of the world.

Beetles as human food

For most people in the over-developed world, the thought of eating insects is repulsive. However, in some regions, beetles and their grubs (larvae) are considered to be a delicacy. In fact, insects play an important part in human nutrition in parts of Africa, Asia and Latin America. The African palm weevil, *Rhynchophorus phoenicis*, which is an important food for many people (DeFoliart, 1992) provides 562Kcal of energy per 100gm, whereas lean beef gives only 219Kcal per 100gm (DeFoliart, 1992).

Why beetles matter

Beetles play important roles as recyclers of detritus and waste products and as predators and herbivores, all helping to maintain the balance of nature.

Beetles also have an economic impact on humans, both as pests of crops and stored food products. For example, since its arrival from Mexico in the late nineteenth century, the Boll

Weevil (Family Curculionidae) has caused $16 billion dollars worth of damage to cotton crops in the USA. The Colorado Beetle (Family Chrysomelidae) is a native of North and Central America and is a pest of members of the plant family Solanaceae, which includes potatoes. This yellow and black stripy beetle is a notifiable quarantine pest, whose introduction is prohibited under the EC law; it even has its own wanted poster! Worldwide, about 20% of all food produced is consumed by insects, though only a small proportion of this is by beetles.

Although no beetles cause serious diseases, some can either bite, burn or blister. Ground beetles (Family Carabidae) are mostly sarcophagous or carnivorous, and, among the larger species, the mandibles can inflict a painful bite. In Britain, one very common garden species, *Pterostichus madidus*, which is about 15mm long, black and often with reddish legs, sometimes bites unwary picnickers.

Bombardier beetles, *Brachinus* spp., as their name implies, have a nasty little trick up their sleeve. When attacked by predators, or handled by an unsuspecting naturalist, it 'explodes' a hot mix of chemicals from its rear end, making an audible pop and a burning sensation on the skin. Blister beetles (Family Meloidae) produce a sticky yellow fluid from their knee joints when attacked or handled. This fluid contains a chemical toxin called cantharidin, a well-known vesicant (blister-causing substance) that is quickly absorbed upon contact and causes inflammation and blistering of the skin.

For mammals, the lethal dose of cantharidin is approximately 1 milligram per kilogram of body weight. Thus, about 200 blister beetles have sufficient toxin to kill an adult horse, and it would take less than twenty to kill a human adult! It therefore seems most peculiar that Spanish Fly, *Lytta vesicatoria*, which is a type of blister beetle, should have been dried and taken as an aphrodisiac. The Marquis de Sade, the French writer legendary for his debauched lifestyle, popularised the fallacy that Spanish Fly is an aphrodisiac. Apparently, he covertly administered cantharidin to several women, with the aim of igniting their passions, and was later prosecuted for poisoning them. These supposed properties of cantharidin are supported neither by theory nor experiment. Thankfully, the modern 'Spanish Fly' aphrodisiac contains no beetle ingredients.

Beetles in the service of man

However, not all beetles are bad, indeed without some species we would be in deep trouble. The dung beetles (Family Scarabaeidae), along with their accompanying fauna and flora, help remove the 100 billion kg of dung that is produced everyday, which is enough dung to keep Victoria Falls flowing continuously.

In Australia, dung beetles are considered to be heroes. Cattle were brought to Australia with the first settlers from Europe. Unfortunately, the native dung beetles are adapted to kangaroo droppings and were unable to cope with cattle dung. So, with time and several million cows, the dung accumulated, which lead to millions of hectares of grazing land being covered. This encouraged the growth of rank grasses, which the cattle did not eat.

Then the flies moved in. Two species, the buffalo fly and the bush fly, both of which breed in dung, soon became serious pests. This caused major problems for farmers and cows alike, as well as the invention of hats fringed with corks. Finally, someone had the bright idea of importing dung beetles from Africa and Europe to deal with the problem. Now, thankfully, about 20 species are keeping the place tidy and relatively free of annoying flies.

Ladybirds are probably the most well-known and popular beetles. They have not only been the source of a nursery rhyme but are now also probably the most successful biological pest control agents to date. In 1887, the Californian citrus crops were under attack from the Cottony Cushion scale insect, *Icerya purchasi*, which had accidentally been introduced from Australia. The Vedalia ladybird, *Rodalia cardinalis*, a natural predator of this scale in Australia, was introduced over a few years, and, by 1890, the harvest underwent a three-fold increase and the Californian citrus industry was saved.

Most of the 5,200 species of ladybird are predators of soft-bodied invertebrates, such as aphids, scale insects, whitefly and mites and as such they contribute substantially to the control of pests in both gardens and on farms.

There are about 40,000 species of Ground beetles (Family Carabidae) in the world, a large proportion of which are predators of soil-dwelling invertebrates, including pests such as slugs and snails. Both the larval and adult stages are among the most common and valuable natural enemies of pests in the garden and farmland. The black ground beetle, *Pterostichus melanarius*, consumes up to three times its own weight daily of soft bodied invertebrates, such as slugs and caterpillars. This is equivalent to about 0.5g of food per day or about 20 medium sized slugs per season!

Beetles are also important predators of aphids in cereal crops and are important control agents of cabbage root fly, a notorious pest of *Brassica* crops. Other specialist beetles pollinate flowers while others re-cycle either dead vegetation, wood or dead animals. Some are scavengers in the nests of birds and mammals and help rid them of fleas and lice.

It is clear that beetles are major links in nearly all terrestrial habitats and food chains. Although often perceived as horrible 'creepy crawlies' or 'pests', the vast majority are either indirectly or directly beneficial or, at the very least, benign.

The British beetle fauna and its conservation 3

With around 4,000 species in 95 families, the beetle fauna of the British Isles is, nevertheless, impoverished compared to that of mainland Europe.

The first book dedicated to British beetles was published over 200 years ago, and since then there have been many identification guides, specialised journals and popular guides published; there are now even numerous websites all about our beetles. Unfortunately, there is still no one book or guide that covers all our beetles. This, along with the fact that the identification of some species requires examination of characters under a microscope, has meant that most people have been dissuaded from studying beetles.

A number of beetles will be familiar because they are attracted to house lights at night. These include cockchafers (Family Scarabaeidae), longhorns (Family Cerambycidae - see front cover) and dor beetles (Family Geotrupidae). The Cockchafer or Maybug, *Melolontha melolontha* (Plate 7) emerges in May (hence the name), sometimes in such large numbers that it can become a public nuisance. Dor beetles are found throughout Britain and the adults, which range in size from 15-25mm, have brilliant metallic blue or purple under parts. These beetles excavate burrows up to 200mm under herbivore dung, where they make a brood chamber for their young.

Some beetles make a noise using a mechanism called stridualtion. Here, the beetle rubs together two specialised parts of the body to generate sounds. A number of beetles stridulate, though we don't always get to hear it. The red and black sexton beetles, *Nicrophorus* spp. (Family Silphidae) are great exponents. These useful beetles bury the carcasses of dead animals, such as mice and birds. Underground, the male and female work as a team, removing fur/feathers from the corpse. They then roll it into a ball and cover it in saliva, which prevents the growth of moulds. They also care for the eggs by eating any predators. Once the eggs hatch, the parental bond grows even stronger; the parents stay with the young and feed them with regurgitated food, stridulating to call their young to dinner!

More vital statistics
- The largest British beetles:
  Stag beetle (*Lucanus cervus*; Family Lucanidae - Plate 11): 28-70mm.
  The great silver water beetle (*Hydrophilus piceus*; Family Hyrdrophilidae): 38-48mm.

- The smallest British Beetle
  The feather-wing beetle (*Acrotrichus chevrolati*; Family): 0.45mm

- Beetle families with the largest number of species in Britain:
  Staphylinidae (Rove beetles - Plate 3): 1,083
  Curculionidae (Weevils - Plates 13 & 14): 480
  Carabidae (Ground beetles - Plates 1 & 2): 360
  Chrysomelidae (Leaf beetles - Plates 18 - 22): 260
  These four families account for nearly 50% of all British beetle species.

- Smallest family of beetles in Britain:
  There are 15 families with just one British species.
  55% of British beetle families have 10 or fewer pecies.

The Conservation of Beetles

With increased demands on land and loss of natural habitats through agriculture, housing, industrialisation and even leisure activities, there are increasing concerns for the plight of British wildlife. We have already seen the extinction in Britain of over 50 beetle species, and at present more than 15% of our beetles are either in decline or are restricted to only a handful of sites.

The Wildlife and Countryside Act 1981 provides legal protection for species listed in its Schedule 5, which are protected from disturbance, injury, intentional destruction or sale. To date, eight species of British beetle receive some form protection under this Act.

There is recent and growing interest in the conservation needs of insects, which has for so long been a neglected issue. This welcome trend has stimulated a number of good publications on insect conservation (see Further Reading), several government based incentives, such as the Biodiversity Actions Plans. Of equal importance are the enhanced roles of non-governmental organisations such as the Wildlife Trusts, the Royal Society for the Protection of Birds, and the National Trust. The most recent addition to these bodies is Buglife: The Invertebrate Conservation Trust, the first organisation in Europe dedicated to the conservation of invertebrates.

Everybody likes to see birds and most people are in favour of conserving them, but what do these birds eat? The answer, for many of them, is insects! So if we want to encourage and sustain our popular garden birds, it pays to think of how to enhance the diversity of insects at a local level.

Encouraging garden beetles

It is impossible to make a list of all the beetles that could occur in a "typical" British or European garden. Each garden will have its own distinctive fauna, which will be dependant on many factors, such as where the garden is situated, the nature of the garden itself, including soil type and plants grown and to what extent pesticides are used. With a British beetle fauna comprising 4000+ species, compiling such a garden list would be quite an undertaking, which would require access to a microscope and an extensive library; many closely related species can only be distinguished by examining diagnostic features that are microscopic.

However, some beetle specialists and garden ecologists have tried. In southeast London, a well-known coleopterist has so far recorded 805 species of beetles in his garden. It has to be said, though, that this list was built up over many years and by an expert who sampled his garden beetles on a regular basis. In a suburban garden in Leicester, ecologist Jennifer Owen recorded 251 species, but recognises that this is a far from complete list, there being many species which are as yet unidentified. It is likely, therefore, that while the average suitable garden will have over a hundred species of beetles living within its confines, the owners will be largely unaware of them.

Not all garden beetles are pests, though the ones we tend to notice are those damaging our plants. The wholesale use of pesticides should be avoided whenever possible, as this will kill not only pest insects, but will also all other insects in the garden. This can lead to an imbalance between pests and their natural predators and parasites, reduced numbers of pollinators and a general decrease in the garden's biodiversity.

At a time when many of our native plants and animals are threatened by intensive agriculture and building development, gardens are becoming increasingly important refuges for wildlife. Indeed, the total area of domestic gardens exceeds that of national nature reserves.

In London, the garden habitat plays an important role in the continued survival of the Stag Beetle, *Lucanus cervus* (Plate 11). In the recent national survey of this species, over 75% of records came from urban and suburban gardens, with very few from more rural areas (Smith, 2003). In a survey of subterranean beetles in suburban gardens, a total of 60 species were collected, of which four are considered to be of conservation importance (Owen, 1999).

Making a beetle friendly garden

There are many ways to make a garden more attractive to insects: plant native species of plants, make a pond, compost heap and leave dead wood in marginal areas. All such measures can increase available habitats, but all of this is negated if the liberal use of pesticides continues. There are a now a large number of guides, books and websites available on 'making a wildlife garden', and these should be consulted for a much more detailed account.

Native Plants

Some native plants, most notably shrubs (e.g. sallow) and trees (e.g. oak), will support a huge variety of insects, since they have had a long time to co-evolve together. Conversely some 'exotic' garden plants, notably many flowers (e.g. lavender), offer a bounty of nectar and pollen unequalled by many of our native species. However, a large proportion of phytophagous beetles are specific to one or a few native plant species, and though there may be plenty of nectar and pollen available for adults to feed on, with no suitable host plants for larval development, they will not breed on site.

In the South of England, one garden was surveyed for weevils over a twenty-year period with 42 species being recorded. Of these, 45% were associated with original native plants, 29% with garden cultivars and 21% with ruderal weeds. Only 5% shared both native and garden plants. This example of just one family of beetles shows that the use of native plants in a garden is beneficial to beetle diversity.

While most people regard the common stinging nettle as a nasty weed, it provides a home and food for numerous moths, butterflies and true bugs. It also has six species of beetle restricted to it, as well as providing a valuable source of food (aphids) for ladybirds.

Some general tips

- Leave some areas in the garden to develop naturally.

- Allow plants to go to seed, because many insects develop in seed heads.

- In vegetable plots, allow some ruderal weeds to grow.

- Dead and dying plants should be left in situ whenever possible or, if removed, placed on a compost heap.

- If you want to grow decorative plants, think about using varieties of trees and shrubs derived from our native types.

- Use species of trees and shrubs that occur naturally in the lanes, hedges and woods in your area.

- Remember, though, that some exotic shrubs are valuable to garden wildlife - often because they supply abundant food (like buddleia for butterflies) or dense, thorny shelter used for hibernation sites.

- Traditional cottage garden plants tend to favour wildlife.

- A high diversity of plants will mean a higher diversity of beetles. Members of the plant families Apiaceae (umbel family), Asteraceae (daisy family), Brassicaceae (cabbage family), Lamiaceae (sage, thyme, oregano and lavender family) and Polygonaceae are particularly good host plants for beetles.

- Avoid double or treble-flowered varieties. Here, the sexual parts of the flower have been converted, by selective breeding, to extra whorls of petals; such flowers therefore produce no pollen and often no nectar and are therefore of no use to flower-visiting insects.

Dead wood

There are more than 1000 species of invertebrates in Britain that depend on dead wood for their survival. The fauna and flora of dead wood are amongst the most threatened organisms in Europe. By retaining dead and rotting wood in the garden, you can encourage invertebrates and fungi. It is a good idea to have different types of wood and at different stages of decay so as to cater for different insects that have different requirements. As well as encouraging insects, this will also provide a nesting site for birds and highways for small mammals and amphibians such as frogs and toads, which also help to eat pests in your garden.

There are many ways to keep dead wood in the garden, the two most common are to leave wood *in situ* where it dies or to create a log pile. The log pile is best situated in a shady part of the garden where it will not become too dry.

Compost heaps

The compost heap, as well as providing a home for insects, is one of the best and cheapest ways of adding nutrients back to your garden. There are four main types of composting: tumble bin, prefabricated, heap and build your own. All achieve the same result and use the same basic techniques, layering fleshy organic waste, adding a small amount of liquid and covering to generate heat. However, of these the 'heap' is the best for insects, as its open plan allows for easy access. Several beetle groups have a particular fondness for compost heaps, such as the feather-wing beetles (Ptiliidae), ant-like beetles (Anthicidae), some of the terrestrial members of the water scavenger beetles (Hydrophilidae) and numerous rove beetles (Staphylinidae).

Refugia

This term is used for habitats used by insects as a shelter or refuge. In a garden, bits of stone, rocks (e.g. in the rockery), dead wood, hedges, grass tussocks, ivy covered trees and walls, leaf litter, all act as 'hiding' places for insects. Some groups, such as the ground beetles and rove beetles use these refugia to hide away during the day, waiting for their nocturnal forays into the garden. Others, such as the leaf beetles and ladybirds will use these sites to hibernate during the winter. Whenever possible, most of these habitats should be left in situ, though, as an aid to keeping the garden tidy, they can be removed to the borders or to a 'wildlife area'.

It is possible to buy ladybird houses or special refugia for these valuable natural pest control agents (See Appendix 1).

Common Garden Beetles: family and species portraits 4

With so many species to deal with, this can only be a very basic guide to some of the beetles that may be encountered in the garden. The species shown in the plates have been chosen for two reasons. First, they illustrate the general features of the families they belong to. Second, with our combined total of 57 years working in museums, these are the beetles most frequently brought to us for identification.

For more detailed accounts of the British beetle fauna and its identification, see the books listed in Further Reading.

Ground Beetles (Family: Carabidae - Plates 1 & 2)
The Carabidae is one of the largest beetle families in the world, with some 40,000 species. The British Isles have around 360 species. As their name implies they live predominantly on the ground and are among the most frequently encountered beetles. Ground beetles are recognised by their well-developed mandibles, long legs and thread like antennae. Most species are black or dark brown, often with a metallic lustre, though some of the diurnal species are brightly coloured with red and black.

Ground beetles are usually omnivorous, feeding on live soft bodied invertebrates, carrion and plant material. Some species are specialist feeders, such as *Loricera pilicornis*, which feeds exclusively on springtails (Collembola) and *Carabus intricatus*, which feeds on slugs and snails. Some species are specialist seed-feeders.

There are usually three larval stages or instars before pupation. The larvae of most ground beetles are carnivorous, except for those of the subfamily Harpalinae, which feed on seeds. The larvae use external digestion, that is, they regurgitate digestive juices on to the food, which becomes liquefied. The larva then sucks up the resulting fluid.

Ground beetles are important predators of economically important pests in agricultural systems, and are now being encouraged by sympathetic management.

There are several carabid species which are common in British gardens. Most of these are beneficial, being active predators and scavengers of soft-bodied invertebrates, such as slugs, caterpillars and aphids.

Plate 1. A Violet Ground Beetle, *Carabus violaceus* (Family: Carabidae).
© Premaphotos Wildlife, Ken Preston-Mafham.

The Violet ground beetle, *Carabus violaceus*, (Plate 1) is one of the largest garden beetles. It is 20-30mm long, black with metallic purple margins to the elytra and pronotum. It is found in gardens and arable land, living under stones, loose bark and in plant litter. It is an active nocturnal predator and scavenger with a particular fondness for slugs

The Strawberry beetle, *Harpalus rufipes*, (Plate 2), is one of a group of seed feeding ground beetles. It is 10-17mm long, black, with the elytra densely clothed with short, conspicuous golden hairs and with red legs. The strawberry beetle is very common in grassland, gardens, arable land, waste ground etc. This species, as its name implies, is sometimes a pest of strawberries

Species of *Amara* are the small, oval, often bronzy or metallic green carabids frequently seen running about grass after being disturbed by the mower. The adults of these beetles feed on seeds and other plant material, though as larvae they are thought to be predators or scavengers. *Amara* species range in size from 4.5-12mm and three or four are often found in gardens. They are especially common in spring, when they have emerged from hibernation and are flying around in search of new habitats.

Rove Beetles (Family: Staphylinidae - Plate 3)
With 46,000 species worldwide, rove beetles comprise one of the largest families of beetles in the world, and are the largest family in Britain, with some 1,083 species. They range in size from 0.6-30mm. In the tropics, perhaps only 25% of species are known to science.

Adult staphylinids are typically elongate and slender, with short elytra, leaving from 3 to 6 abdominal segments exposed. The antennae of most species are long and bead-like, though some species have a club at the end. Most species are black, sometimes with red

Plate 2. A Strawberry beetle, *Harpalus rufipes* (Family: Carabidae). © Clive R. Turner.

or yellow markings. A few species are brightly coloured, with red, orange or yellow and black markings and a few are metallic hued.

The family is very diverse in biology and preferred habitats range from the semi-aquatic, to fungi and dung. Some live in caves, others scavenge in the nests of small mammals. Most species are saprophagous or predatory as both larvae and adults, feeding on a range of soft-bodied invertebrates. The larvae of a few species eat algae or fungi.

The immature stages usually develop rapidly, from a few days to a few weeks, whereas the adults are long-lived. As a general rule, staphylinids are beneficial predators of pest insects.

The Devil's Coach Horse (*Staphylinus olens* - Plate 3) is one of the largest rove beetles in Britain, being up to 30mm long. It is active throughout the year, most often being seen between April and October, although it is sometimes found hibernating under the bark of dead trees and under large stones. Its habitats range range from woodlands and meadows, to gardens and hedgerows. The devil's Coach-Horse is a fast moving, voracious carnivore. It can fly but prefers to spend most of its life on the ground, under debris and leaf litter. The other popular name for this beetle is 'cock-tail', because of it raises its tail like a scorpion when threatened. It cannot sting but it does have chemical defence at its disposal: a pair of white glands at the end of the abdomen emit a foul smell and it can also squirt a brown fluid from its mouth and anus.

Ladybirds (Family: Cocinellidae - Plates 4 - 6)
About fifty species of ladybird occur in Britain; of these, the vast majority are beneficial to the gardener, being avid predators of garden pests. The family comprises over 5,200 species worldwide, ranging in size from just 0.8mm to over 10mm. Most coccinellids look

like the typical ladybirds, in being patterned with red and black or yellow and black. However, a large number of the smaller species are uniformly coloured and hairy (pubescent). Ladybirds generally have an oval-oblong domed body, short antennae, with a terminal 3 segmented club and spoon-like maxillary palps.

A single female lays up to 1,500 yellow eggs, usually in batches of between 20 and 40. The eggs hatch after about four days. The larva (Plate 4) passes through three instars, after which the pupa is formed (Plate 5). The adult emerges from this after about two weeks (Plate 6).

Ladybirds become active around March, usually, in the case of predatory species, when the aphids have emerged. Most ladybirds prey on soft bodied invertebrates, particularly aphids. Some species feed on mildews, and two species in Britain are phytophagous.

The Seven-spot Ladybird (*Coccinella 7-punctata* - Plates 4 - 6) and the Two-spot Ladybird, *Adalia 2-punctata*, are often referred to as the 'gardeners friends', because they have a particular liking for aphids. These are probably the most frequently encountered species in inner city areas and gardens. The Two-spot ladybird is generally red with a pair of black spots on the elytra, with a pair of white marks covering most of the side of the pronotum and a smaller pair centrally on the pronotal base. The larvae are dark grey, with dark tubercles and with three spots in a triangular pattern. The Seven-spot Ladybird is one of our largest ladybirds, being up to 8mm in length; the elytra are red and have seven distinctive black spots, three on each side of the elytra and one large central spot at the base that often has a pair of white spots at either side. The larva is generally slate grey-blue, with four pairs of yellow-orange spots.

Plate 3. The Devil's Coachhorse, *Staphylinus olens* (Family: Staphylinidae). © Premaphotos Wildlife, Ken Preston-Mafham.

Plate 4. A larva of the Seven-spot Ladybird, *Coccinella septempunctata* (Family: Coccinellidae). © Clive R. Turner.

Plate 5. A pupa of the Seven-spot Ladybird, *Coccinella septempunctata* (Family: Coccinellidae). © Clive R. Turner.

Chafers (Family: Scarabaeidae - Plates 7 - 10)

Worldwide, the chafer family" contains some 27,800 species, of which over 18,000 are "true" chafers. There are around ten species of chafer in Britain, of which three are commonly found in gardens. The family also includes the dung beetles.

Chafers are recognised by their asymmetrical, fan-like antennae (Plate 7) and the last segment of the abdomen being exposed beyond the elytra. When handled, some chafers make a squeaking sound by rubbing a row of pegs on its hind legs against its middle legs. Adult chafers feed on the leaves of bushes and trees, whereas the larvae live underground, feeding on roots, detritus and rotting wood. The larvae of some chafers are sometimes a pest of lawns, and are often dug up by gardeners. The C-shaped larvae are white with a brown head. (Plate 8). They have a strong pair of mandibles for chewing through roots. The rear end of the abdomen is often dark because of a fermentation chamber in which symbiotic bacteria and fungi help the larva to digest its food.

The Cockchafer or May bug, *Melolontha melolontha* (Plate 7), occurs throughout Britain, though is more common in the South. It is light brown, with the head and pronotum being darker. The elytra are covered in tiny grey hairs, which gives them a dusty appearance. Cockchafers measure about 30mm in length, and the abdomen ends in a hardened segment called the pygidium, which has a nodose swelling, a distinctive feature of this beetle.

They are most often seen flying at dusk from May to July, often being attracted to house lights and they sometimes come indoors. Their flight is very haphazard and they often collide with objects as they fly in search of mates. Cockchafers are found in a range of habitats, such as woodland, farmland, and gardens. The adults feed on leaves of trees, especially oaks. The cockchafer has a three-year life cycle. Females lay eggs in the soil and the larvae remain there for a further two years, feeding on roots. The larvae can grow up to 50mm in length.

The metallic green Rose Chafer, *Cetonia aurata* (Plate 9) sometimes occurs in gardens in the south-east of Britain; it is usually seen feeding on flowers during hot and sunny spells in June and July. The larva of this species feed on rotting wood and detritus (Plate 8) and sometimes occur in compost heaps, where it is often mistaken for that of a stag beetle.

Plate 6: An adult Seven-spot Ladybird, Coccinella septempunctata (Family: Coccinellidae). © Clive R. Turner.

Plate 7. A male Cockchafer or May bug, *Melolentha melolontha* (Family: Scarabaeidae) about to launch into flight. The horny elytra (wing cases) are raised, exposing the membranous wings which they protect. Elytra are typical of beetles as a whole, the order Coleoptera. © Premaphotos Wildlife, Ken Preston-Mafham.

However, Rose Chafer larvae move along on theirs backs, are quite hairy and ''firm' to the touch, whereas stag beetle larvae tend to be sedentary, unless poked, have no distinct hairs and are soft to the touch.

The Summer Chafer, *Amphimallon solstitialis*, (Plate 10), is somewhat like the Cockchafer, though is slightly smaller (up to 20mm long), and doesn't have such a pronounced nodose swelling at the tip of the pygidium. Adults are active from June to August, most often at dusk, when large mating swarms aggregate around the tops of bushes and small trees.

Stag beetles (Lucanidae - Plates 11 & 12)
Only four members of this family have occurred in Britain, though one is now extinct. The other three are widespread in the southeast, becoming less common towards the north. Apart from their large mandibles, stag beetles can be recognised by their large size and elbowed antennae, each with a terminal, asymmetrical club. Stag beetles are so-called because the males of many species have large mandibles that resemble the antlers of stags. Males use these to fight each other to establish a dominance hierarchy over a suitable mating platform, usually a fallen log. Fights involve one male grabbing his opponent between his mandibles, and then throwing him over. Females are attracted to dominant males which own such real estate.

There are around 800 species worldwide, most of which live in the tropics. Because of their size and ornamentation (e.g. large mandibles), stag beetles have become 'collectables', and high prices are paid for some species. Thus, many species are now protected by law, including our very own stag beetle!

Plate 8. The C-shaped larva of a Rose Chafer, *Cetonia aurata*. (Family: Scarabaeidae).
© Clive R. Turner.

The larvae of stag beetles resemble those of the chafers, being C-shaped and can often be confused with them. However, stag beetle larvae are nearly always found in dead wood. There is also a behavioural difference, in as much as a stag beetle larva will tend to sit still when placed on a flat surface, whereas most chafer larvae will crawl away.

The Stag Beetle, *Lucanus cervus*, (Plate 11) is the largest British beetle: males grow up to about 70mm in length, including the mandibles, whereas the female grows to approximately 60mm. The head and pronotum are black and the elytra are chestnut brown. The Stag Beetle is most often found south of the Thames in the southeast of England, where it flies between May and August. Males are often seen flying on warm summer evenings in search of mates. Sometimes they are even found 'knocked out' below lampposts, after being attracted to and then bumping into the light.

The adults feed on tree sap and fruits. The larvae eat rotting wood, usually tree stumps and roots particularly of elm, beech and lime. The larvae can take around 3-4 years to develop; they have a soft, cream-coloured, slightly transparent body, with six orange legs. The head is orange and has very sharp brown mandibles. When fully grown, the larvae measure around 80mm long and nearly 20mm thick. This is one of the few beetles in which gardens are one of the most important habitats.

The Lesser Stag Beetle, *Dorcus parallelipidus* (Plate 12), is similar to the female stag beetle, but has an all-black body. This species is somewhat local but widespread in Southern Britain. Larvae feed in rotting wood, especially that of oak and ash. The adults feed on sap of deciduous trees including ash and willow. They are seen between May and September, but are commonest in spring.

Plate 9. A Rose Chafer, *Cetonia aurata* (Family: Scarabaeidae) feeding at hogweed flowers. © Premaphotos Wildlife, Ken Preston-Mafham.

Plate 10. A Summer Chafer, *Amphimallon solstitialis*, (Family: Scarabaeidae). © Clive R. Turner.

Plate 11. A male Stag Beetle, *Lucanus cervus* (Family: Lucanidae) on a log. This species is often common in gardens in south-eastern UK, even in suburban London.
© Premaphotos Wildlife, Rod Preston-Mafham.

Plate 12. A Lesser Stag Beetle, *Dorcus parallelopipedus* (Family: Lucanidae).
© Clive R. Turner.

Plate 13. A Vine Weevil, *Otiorhychus sulcatus* (Family: Curculionidae) in an English garden. This species is often a pest of indoor as well as outdoor plants. © Premaphotos Wildlife, Ken Preston-Mafham.

Weevils (Family: Curculionidae - Plates 13 & 14; Apionidae, - Plate 15)

The weevils are the most species rich group of animals on the planet, with the Curculionidae comprising some 60,000 species. All weevils are phytophagous, and it is thought that the reason for this high diversity of species is that they evolved during the time that the higher plants diversified during the Cretaceous period, some 150 million years ago.

Members of both weevil families, Curculionidae and Apionidae, are easily recognisable by their short to long snout (rostrum) and elbowed antennae with a terminal club. In Britain there are around 480 species, including some which are major pests of both horticultural and agricultural plants. In the garden as well as some of the pest species, species of *Phyllobius* live on stinging nettles and shrubs; they are often covered in metallic green scales.

Weevils have a variety of larval feeding habits, from leaf mining and wood boring to feeding on the outsides of leaves and roots. The leaf mining species leave tell-tail tracks where they feed between the upper and lower section the leaf, which is often seen on beech trees. The larvae of most weevils are recognised by their grub-like appearance, with an obvious dark head and the absence of thoracic legs.

The Vine weevil, *Otiorhynchus sulcatus*, (Plate 13) is known to most gardeners because it is a serious pest of various indoor and outdoor plants. The genus *Otiorhynchus* includes over 800 species, and, of the 22 species found in Britain, at least six are considered introduced.

The adults are long lived, and predominantly polyphagous on woody plants, and despite being flightless, are very mobile. The larvae of most species are polyphagous soil dwelling root-feeders. *Otiorhynchus* can be recognized by their short snouts, stout swollen bodies and enlarged femur on all legs. Most species are brown to black, and are often covered in pale scales and stout hairs or yellow dusting.

Several species are pests in gardens and of indoor plants, with *Otiorhynchus sulcatus* being the most prolific and the one most frequently found by gardeners. This species has the advantage of being parthenogenetic, which means it does not need to mate for reproduction.

Adult *Otiorhyncus* species bite small notches around the edges of leaves in light infestations, producing deep, wavy incisions in heavier infestations. The larvae feed on plant roots and may cause wilting and the collapse of leaves and shoots, leading to death.

The Figwort weevil, *Cionus scrophulariae* (Plate 14) is a rather attractive, rounded weevil, 3-5mm long, patterned with white, yellowish and black pubescence. It is widely distributed and fairly common in southern Britain. The adults and larvae normally feed on figworts in the wild, but also live in gardens as pests of *Phygelius*, *Buddleia* and *Verbascum*. The larva is a distinctive, slug-like grub, which is covered in shining slime.

The Hollyhock stem weevils (*Apion* species) belong to the family Apionidae, which resemble the weevils of the family Curculionidae, but have a more pear shaped body, a longer snout and short, more or less straight antennae situated towards the tip of the snout. In Britain, about four species of *Apion* live on malvaeceous plants, including hollyhock and garden varieties of *Malva*. They are small (2-3mm), mostly blue weevils, that cause small holes in the leaves. The larvae live inside the stems or fruits of the plants. There are several other *Apion* species that may be found in the garden, on plants such as thistles and legumes and one, *Apion* miniatum, (Plate 15), is a specialist on dock leaves.

Plate 14. A Figwort Weevil, *Cionus scophulariae* (Family: Curculioniade). © Clive R. Turner.

Plate 15. The Red Dock Weevil, *Apion miniatum* (Family: Apionidae). © Premaphotos Wildlife, Ken Preston-Mafham.

Click Beetles (Family: Elateridae, Plate 16) are so called because they have a special way of escaping danger: by arching their body, they create tension in a special hinge on the thorax. When the tension is suddenly released, the beetle leaps into the air with an audible click. There are 63 species of click beetle in Britain, and all of them can leap in this way.

Most adult click beetles are more or less parallel sided, with the hind angles of the pronotum extended backwards into a sharp point. The majority of the British click beetles are found in natural habitats, with some species being only found on shingle banks near rivers, whilst others are restricted to breeding in red-rot in old oak trees.

Plate 16. A mating pair of the Garden Click Beetle, *Athous haemorrhadalis* (Family: Elateridae). © Premaphotos Wildlife, Ken Preston-Mafham.

The biology of most species (except those that breed in deadwood) follows the same pattern: the female lays eggs in the soil during early summer and the larvae hatch up to four weeks later. They are known as wireworms because of their elongate, cylindrical shape. They feed mainly in summer, on the underground parts of plants, and may burrow into tubers and corms and become serious pests. The larval stage may last up to five years.

The Garden Click beetle, *Athous haemorrhoidalis* (Plate 16) is 10-15mm long, brown and black and occurs in all type of grassland during May to August. It has a preference for loamy and sandy soils, which are not too dry.

Soldier and Sailor Beetles (Family: Cantharidae - Plate 17) are so called because some species are the same red as pre-20th century British army uniforms. They are sometimes called 'blood suckers', though they do not suck blood!

Soldier beetles are small to medium sized beetles (2-15mm), often brown to grey, or orange to yellowish brown in colour. The adults have soft bodies, which appear flat, the head protrudes forward from the flattened pronotum and the antenna are most often thread-like. The adults are abundant on flowers and foliage where they feed on nectar, pollen, or other insects. The larvae of most species are ground living and carnivorous, though a few species feed on plants. There are over 5,000 species worldwide, but only about forty species occur in Britain, most of which live in wetland and grassland habitats, including gardens and hedgerows. They are active in early to late summer.

The Hogweed Bonking Beetle *Rhagonycha fulva* (Plate 17), so called because of its mating behaviour, is 7-10mm long, orange-red, with black tips to the elytra. It is also known as the Red Soldier Beetle. The adults are very common on umbelliferous flowers in late July, where they are predatory on other insects. The larvae are predatory, and are usually found at base of plants in leaf litter.

Plate 17. The Hogweed Bonking Beetle, *Rhagonycha fulva* (Family: Cantharidae). © Clive R. Turner.

Plate 18. A Broad Bean Beetle, *Bruchus rufimanus* (Family: Chrysomelidae).
© Clive R. Turner.

Leaf beetles (Chrysomelidae - Plates 18 - 22)

Leaf beetles are among the most beautiful of all beetles, with many brightly coloured species, varying from metallic shades of blue, purple and green to burnished gold. They are mostly ovoid and slightly domed, with long thread-like antennae. All 37,000 world species are phytophagous, occurring on all major flowering plant families. Both the larvae and adults live their entire lives on the plant, only venturing away from their host plant to avoid predation, to hibernate or aestivate and to colonise new areas.

Each species lives on one or just a few closely related species of host plant. The larvae of some species mine the leaves, leaving distinctive serpentine trails on the leaf surface, whilst others are external feeders and have a stout, grub-like appearance. Most of the larger species are univoltine, whilst some of the smaller species may be bivoltine or even multivoltine, but this is often dependant on how good a given year is.

The Broad Bean Seed Beetle, *Bruchus rufimanus* (Plate 18) is 4mm long, mottled with black, brown and white scales. These beetles are usually seen by gardeners who use their own seed from a previous crop because the adults leave emergence holes in the dried broad bean seeds.

Plate 19. Two adult Rosemary Beetles, *Chrysolina americana* (Family: Chrysomelidae) feeding at flowers of lavender. © Clive R. Turner.

The Rosemary Beetle, *Chrysolina americana* (Plate 19) is 8mm long and a very attractive metallic green with purple stripes. Despite its Latin name, it is a native of southern Europe. This species has recently become established in Britain and was probably imported with horticultural plants. Since its discovery in Surrey in 1994, it has spread to many areas of London and has been found in Berkshire, Leicestershire and Norfolk. The larvae are greyish white, with five darker longitudinal lines, and, when fully grown, are around 5-8 mm long. Both the adults and the larvae feed on the leaves and flowers of rosemary, lavender, garden sage and thyme.

The adults aestivate during the summer, emerging in late August to breed. The eggs hatch within a couple of weeks, and the larvae will feed for four weeks before entering the soil to pupate. Adults emerge two to three weeks after pupation.

The large metallic green Mint Leaf Beetle, *Chrysolina menthastri* (Plate 20) is often found in gardens feeding on water mint and other mint species.

The Scarlet Lily Beetle, *Lilioceris lilii* (Plate 21) is bright red, 8 mm long and is a serious pest of lilies and fritillaries. In horticultural circles, it is known as the 'scarlet plague'. It is native to southern Europe and first became established in Britain during the 1940s. Both adults and larvae damage lilies, principally by defoliating them, but in severe infestations the flowers and even the stems may be eaten. Although the adult beetles are sometimes found on other plant species, only lilies and fritillaries are the true host plants, on which the eggs are laid and the larvae develop. It is considered to be a serious threat to one of Britain's rarest plants, the Snake's Head Fritillary, *Fritillaria meleagris*.

Plate 20. An adult Mint beetle, *Chrysolina menthastri* (Family: Chrysomelidae) feeding at water mint. © Premaphotos Wildlife, Ken Preston-Mafham.

Plate 21. A Scarlet Lily Beetle, *Lilioceris lilii* (Family: Chrysomelidae) eating a lily petal. © Clive R. Turner.

The Asparagus beetle, *Crioceris asparagi* (Plate 22) is very distinctive, some 6-8 mm long, black in colour with a reddish thorax and sides to the elytra, which also have six yellow blotches. Both adults and larvae feed on asparagus foliage and bark. The beetles usually emerge from hibernation in late spring and lay eggs onto the sprouting asparagus. Larvae are creamy, greyish-black and grow up to 10mm.

Raspberry Beetles (Byturidae - Plate 23)

There are just two members of the family Byturidae in Britain, both of which are widespread in most habitats, though the Raspberry Beetle is the more common of the two.

The Raspberry Beetle, *Byturus tomentosus* (Plate 23) is about 4mm long, and usually brown in colour with conspicuous brick-yellow pubescence. Adults are most often seen feeding on flowers, particularly on umbels such as hogweed. The larvae develop in fruits of bramble and raspberry; they are the common white grubs found in wild fruit. This beetle is very common, and is sometimes a pest of cultivated fruit.

Plate 22. A courting pair of Asparagus Beetles, *Crioceris asparagi* (Family: Chrysomelidae). © Premaphotos Wildlife, Ken Preston-Mafham.

Carpet beetles (Dermestidae - Plate 24)

Carpet beetles (Dermestidae - Plate 24) include several common species that are found in houses, sometimes as pests of woollen carpets. The normal larval food is skin, feather and hair debris in the nests of birds and mammals. There are many different species of carpet beetles. The adults of most species are small, oblong to oval-shaped and between 5-8mm long, with varying degrees of patterning. The two most common species in Britain are the Variegate Carpet Beetle, *Anthrenus vebasci* and the two spotted carpet beetle, *Attagenus pellio*. The latter is 3-6mm long, oblong and black with two pale spots on the elytra.

The Variegate Carpet Beetle, *Anthrenus vebasci* (Plate 24) is 3-5mm long, clothed in white, black and yellowish scales, giving it a zig-zag pattern of light and dark colours. This and a related species are notorious among museum curators, for they are also known as the Museum Beetles, which can devastate insect collections.

The adult beetles are found in spring and early summer, often on the inside of windows, or on flowers in the garden. They feed on nectar and pollen. The larvae are commonly called 'woolly bears' because of their bristly haired appearance and are often found at the edges of carpets, or under household clutter in the back of cupboards and pantries.

Plate 23. A Raspberry Beetle, *Byturus tomentosus* (Family: Byturidae) on bramble.
© Clive R. Turner.

Longhorn Beetles (Cerambycidae - Front cover and Plate 25)
Longhorns get their name from their long antennae, which are often as long as the whole insect. They have broad elytral shoulders and tapering bodies. Worldwide, there are some 25,000 species all, of which are phytophagous as both adults and larvae. Many species are forestry pests because their larvae bore into solid wood, damaging large stands of timber. However, not all longhorn beetles live on in dead or dying wood: some species feed on herbaceous plants such as hogweed, while others are root feeders. Most of the 64 British species are found in woodlands and hedgerows during the spring and early summer, often sitting on flowers where they feed on pollen and nectar. The larvae of all species are legless, elongate and grub-like with a darkened head, and are usually only found by digging into their host plant.

The Maculate Longhorn, *Strangalia maculata* (Front cover) is large, black and yellow, and is found throughout southern Britain in early summer. The adults are most often seen on hawthorn and umbel flowers, particularly along woodland rides and hedgerows. They also visit flowers in gardens. The larvae develop in dead wood, often in smallish branches.

The Wasp Beetle, *Clytus arietis*, (Plate 25) is a medium black-brown and yellow striped longhorn beetle, which is thought to be a wasp-mimic. The adults are found on flowers where they feed on pollen and nectar. The larvae live in the dead timber of hardwood trees, usually that of willows and birch.

Plate 24. An adult Variegate Carpet Beetle, *Anthrenus verbasci* (Family: Dermestidae). Sometimes called the Museum Beetle, this individual is feeding on pollen at hogweed flowers. © Clive R. Turner.

Plate 25. A Wasp beetle, *Clytus arietus* (Family: Cerambycidae) at an ox-eye daisy. © Premaphotos Wildlife, Ken Preston-Mafham.

Frequently asked questions 5

Do beetles bite?

Most beetles can bite, since they have mandibulate mouthparts. However, only a few of the larger beetles can bite and hurt. The stag beetles, Lucanus cervus (Plate 11) and *Dorcus parallelipidus*, (Plate 12), the Great Diving beetle, *Dytiscus marginalis*, and some of the larger longhorns and ground beetles can all give a bit of a nip, though rarely do they pierce the skin. The best way to pick up a beetle is with a spoon or trowel, and then either place it in a clean and dry jam-jar or simply move it to where you want it to go. The braver reader can simply grab the beetle by the thorax, just behind the head, thus negating the jaws!

Are beetles poisonous?

Some beetles have what is called aposomatic colouration, that is, they have warning colours. These are usually combinations of black and/or red or yellow. Bright, "warning" colour patterns signal to potential predators that the beetle is harmful in some way, such as having a defensive secretion which could be either poisonous or distasteful. Birds and mammals soon learn to associate the colour pattern with an unpleasant experience and avoid future contact. Adult ladybirds (Plate 6), for example, are warningly coloured because they release an orange-red, bitter tasting secretion from between their knee joints when disturbed (reflex bleeding).

There are, however, some cunning exceptions to this rule. Like many other insects, some beetles are warningly coloured although they pack no chemical punch. These species mimic the colour patterns of other species which are poisonous. In adopting this strategy, the mimic exploits the ability of predators to associate a colour pattern with distasteful prey without investing in the chemical hardware. The Wasp Beetle (Plate 26) is aptly named, since it mimics the common wasp. A wasp can sting and most large predators err on the side of safety: if you look like a dangerous bug, no one is going to try and eat you.

Where do the pest beetles come from?

Since most beetles can fly, garden pests will have flown into neighbouring plots or from local countryside. Flightless species, such as the Vine Weevil, *Otiorhynchus sulcatus* (Plate 13) either simply walk from a neighbour's garden or, more usually, are imported into your garden with plants from a garden centre or nursery. Because beetle larvae are hard to spot, they are easily transported around, often in old stems or in plant-pot soil.

How do I know if beetles are eating my plants?

Most beetles leave distinctive feeding holes, although, as larvae, many species may be inside the plant tissue or feeding below ground on the roots and therefore go unnoticed until the plant starts to wilt or die. Feeding damage may be in the form of notched or crenulated leaf margins, as made by vine weevils or 'shot holes' as made by flea beetles and *Apion* weevils (Plate 15). In severe cases leaves may be completely destroyed, with just skeletal remains of the veins.

In most cases, adult beetles can be found on the plants, though with each species the time of appearance in the year will differ. Because many species are nocturnal and hide away at the base of plants or in debris during the day, it is always wise to check the plants at dusk, or later in the night with a torch.

Leafcutter bees also leave a notched leaf, though this tends to be completely semi-circular, whereas in most beetles the notch has rough edges. Slugs generally leave a trail of slime over leaves or at the base of the plant where they have fed.

How do I get rid of weevils and leaf beetles eating my plants?

The best way to rid plants of pest beetles is to pick them off by hand. Pesticides should be a last resort because these will kill everything, not just the target species. Since many pest beetles are nocturnal, it is best to go out at night with a torch and hand pick them from the plants. Alternatively, place a tray, washing up bowl or even an upturned umbrella, under the plant and give it a firm tap. The beetles should then fall off into the receptacle and can then either be released in a 'wild area' or be disposed of with boiling hot water. Sticky traps and barriers are other alternatives to spraying and can now be bought in most garden centres, as can biological control agents such as nematode worms. However, if all else fails and pesticide treatment is decided upon, then contact suitable garden centres or horticultural societies for advice on the best pesticide and its application. ALWAYS remember that spraying insecticides on plants that are in flower should be confined to dusk so as to avoid harming bees.

Glossary

Abdomen: the third and hindmost part of the three principle body parts of the insect, usually comprising of 9-10 segments, though not all may be visible.

Aestivating (Aestivation): a period of dormancy during the warmer summer months.

Anelytrous: without trace of wing cases (elytra).

Bivoltine: passing though two life cycles in one year.

Coprophagous: feeding on dung.

Diapause: a period during which growth or development is suspended and physiological activity is reduced. In temperate climates this mostly occurs in winter.

Diurnal: being active during the day.

Ectoparasite: a parasite that lives on the outside of its host's body.

Elytra: the modified front wings of a beetle, hardened to form a protective case for the membranous hind wings.

Genera: the plural of genus.

Genus: a division of classification, which encompasses a group of species that share a combination of similar characteristics unique to that group.

Family: a division of classification, which encompasses a group of genera that share a combination of characters unique to that group.

Instar(s): the stage of an insect between moults.

Larviform: of those species of beetles which, as adults, retain all the characteristics of the larvae, except that they have functioning gonads (testes & ovaries) and genitalia.

Mandibulate: possessing mandibles (jaws).

Multivoltine: passing through more than two life cycles in one year.

Mycophagous: feeding on fungi.

Omnivorous: feeding on both plants and animals.

Phytophagous: feeding on plants.

Polyphagous: feeding upon a wide variety of animal, plants, fungal matter.

Saprophagous: feeding on detritus and decaying organic matter of both plant and animal origin.

Sarcophagous: feeding on dead animals.

Parasite: an organism that lives on another animal (the host), usually gaining food directly from its host. The host is not killed.

Parasitoid: an insect whose larvae are parasites that eventually kill their hosts.

Polyphagous: feeding on many types of food, including animal and plant material.

Prothorax: the first part of the thorax. The thorax is divided into three parts the pro-, meso- and the metathorax.

Pubescent: covered in short hairs.

Saprophagous: feeding on decaying or decayed organic matter.

Sarcophagous: feeding upon animal corpses.

Species: a taxonomic division, ranking below a genus and consisting of populations of related individuals capable of interbreeding. This is represented by an un-capitalized Latinised adjective or noun following a capitalized genus name (See Genus, above). Latin names of genera and species are italicised or underlined when written.

Stridulation: the production of sound, usually by rubbing together two parts of the body with specially modified surface sculpturing, a peg or series of pegs against the file, a series of fine, transverse ridges.

Synanthropic: associated with humans and their dwellings.

Tarsi: the distal part of the leg of an arthropod, divided into segments. In beetles it is the fifth part of the leg, consisting of between 3-5 segments, usually ending in a claw.

Univoltine: passing through one complete life cycle in a year.

Xylophagous: feeding on wood.

References, further reading and useful contacts

Bernard, P. C., 1999. *Identifying British Insects and Arachnids. An annotated bibliography of key works.* Cambridge University Press. 353pp.

Booth, R. G., Cox, M.L. & Madge, R. B., 1990. *IIE Guides to Insects of Importance to Man.* 3. Coleoptera. IIE & NHM, London. 384pp.

Buczacki, S. & Harris, K., 1981. *Collins Guide to the Plant Pests, Diseases and Disorders of Garden Plants.* Harper Collins, London. 512pp.

Camberfort, Y., 1994. *Beetles as Religious Symbols.* Cultural Entomology 2: 15-23.

Chinery, M., 1986. *Collins Guide to Insects of Britain and Western Europe.* Collins. 319pp.

Chinery, M., 1993. *Field Guide to the Insects of Britain and Northern Europe.* Collins. 448pp

Cooter, J. (Editor), 1991. *A Coleopterist's Handbook.* Amateur Entomologists' Society, Middlesex. 294pp.

Defoliart, G., 1992. Insects as human food: Gene DeFoliart discusses some nutritional and economic aspects. *Crop Protection* **11**: 395-399.

Evans, A. E. & Bellamy, C.L., 2000. *An inordinate fondness for beetles.* University of California Press. 208 pages.

Grissell, E., 2001. *Insects and Gardens: in pursuit of a garden ecology.* Timber Press, Portland, Oregon, USA. 345pp.

Hodge, P. J. & Jones, R. A., 1995. *New British Beetles,* Species not in Joy's Handbook. British Journal of Natural History Society, Reading. 175pp.

Hyman, P. S. (revised Parsons, M.S.), 1992. UK Nature Conservation No. 3: *A review of the scarce and Threatened Coleoptera of Great Britain part 1* Joint Nature Conservation Committee, Peterborough. 484pp.

Hyman, P. S. (revised Parsons, M.S.), 1994. UK Nature Conservation No. 12: *A review of the scarce and threatened Coleoptera of Great Britain. Part 2.* Joint Nature Conservation Committee, Peterborough. 267pp.

Joy, N. H., 1932. *A Practical Handbook of British Beetles.* Witherby, London, 1976 reprint by E.W. Classey, Volumes 1: 622pp & Volume 2: 194pp.

Lawrence, J. F. & Newton, A. F., 1982. Evolution and classification of beetles. *Annual Review of Ecology and Systematics* **13**: 261-290.

Mann, D. J., 2002. *Ladybirds: natural pest control.* Osmia Publications, Ltd., Banbury. 40pp

O'Toole, C., 1995. *Alien Empire: an exploration of the lives of insects.* BBC Publications, 224pp. [The book of the BBCtv series.]

O'Toole, C. (Ed.), 2002. *The New Encyclopedia of Insects and Their Allies,* Oxford University Press. 240pp.

Owen, J., 1991. *The ecology of a garden. The first fifteen years.* Cambridge University Press, Cambridge, UK. 403pp.

Owen, J. A., 1999. Suburban gardens in south-west London as homes for subterranean beetles. *Entomologist's Record and Journal of Variation* **111**(1) : 11-19.

McGavin, G.,C., 2000. Dorling Kindersley Handbooks: *Insects, spiders and other terrestrial arthropods.* Dorling Kindersley. 255pp.

McGavin, G. C., 2001. *Essential Entomology: an order by order introduction.* Oxford University Press. 318pp.

Savigear, A., 1992. *Garden Pests and Predators: the wildlife in your garden and its ecological control.* Blandford, London. 128pp. ,

Smith, M., 2003. *National Stag Beetle Survey 2002.* London, People's Trust for Endangered Species. 14pp.

Tilling, S. M., 1987. *A Guide to the major groups of British terrestrial invertebrates.* Field Studies Council. 71pp.

Wheather, C. P. & Cook, P. A., 2003. *Studying Invertebrates.* Naturalists' Handbook. Richmond Publishing Co. 120pp.

USEFUL JOURNALS, SOCIETIES AND WEBSITES

The Coleopterist is Britain's leading journal for the study of beetles. It is published three times a year and each issue contains a mix of papers, short notes, reviews, subscriber notices and literature notices on British beetles. The website http://www.coleopterist.org.uk/ contains a photo gallery, information on where to find beetles, contact addresses and other useful information on beetles.

The Coleoptera website contains information on world beetles and includes many useful links. It can be found at: http://www.coleoptera.org/index.htm

The Tree of Life website gives information on the classification of beetles.

http://tolweb.org/tree?group=Coleoptera&contgroup=Endopterygota

The Coleopterist Society is a North American group dedicated to the study of beetles.

http://www.coleopsoc.org/

Waterbeetle World is a site for aquatic beetles.

http://www.zo.utexas.edu/faculty/sjasper/beetles/index.htm

SOCIETIES

British Entomological and Natural History Society

The British Entomological & Natural History Society (BENHS) is a society for both amateur and professional entomologists; its aims are the promotion and advancement of research in entomology, with an increasing emphasis on the conservation of the fauna and flora of Britain.

Contact address: The Pelham-Clinton Building, Dinton Pastures Country Park, Davis Street, Hurst, Reading, Berkshire, RG10 0TH

http://www.benhs.org.uk/

Amateur Entomologist's Society

Is a group for those with an interest specifically in entomology, but also in natural history in general. The society's aim is to promote the study of entomology, especially among amateurs and the younger generation.

Contact address: The AES, PO Box 8774, London, SW7 5ZG

The Bug Club

The junior wing of the AES, The Bug Club is aimed at young people and the "Young at heart" who find insects and other creepy crawlies fascinating.

http://www.ex.ac.uk/bugclub/main.html

Appendix 1:
Ladybird Houses

The ladybird house designed and marketed by the Oxford Bee Company Ltd. provides ladybirds not only with a place to roost on cold nights in spring and autumn, but also with a safe haven in which to hibernate over winter. It comes with complete instructions.

Each ladybird house comprises a box made of environmentally friendly plastic, with a louvered door (Plate 26). Inside are many roosting/hibernation chambers made out of honeycombed, re-cycled cardboard (Plate 27). The inclined slats of the louvered door exploit a characteristic behaviour of nearly all insects: when they land on an inclined surface, they invariably walk upwards, against gravity. In this way, ladybirds are "invited" into the refuge. Those other useful, aphid-eating insects, lacewings, will also use the ladybird house.

The ladybird house comes with a complete set of instructions on installation and maintenance and can be purchased direct from:

The Ladybird House is distributed for the Oxford Bee Co. by CJ Wildbirdfoods Ltd., Rea, Upton Magna, Shrewsbury, Shropshire SY4 4UR. E-mail: commercial@birdfood.co.uk. Tel: 01743 709555; Fax: 01743 709505.

Plate 26: A ladybird house fixed to a garden wall. © Oxford Bee Co. Ltd.

Plate 27: A ladybird house with the front door partly opened to reveal roosting/hibernation chambers. This inner section can be removed for cleaning. © Oxford Bee Co. Ltd.